# This is My D

Written and Illustrated by Patricia Marie Bongiovi

This is my dog.

He is my buddy.

# I give him a bath

# This is my dog.

# He is never rude.

# He stands up tall

# And nibbles his food.

# This is my dog.

# He lets me know

WOOF
WOOF

DRINK
PLEASE

# When he wants a drink.

This is my dog.

# He walks by my side.

# When I sit in my wagon,

He gives me a ride.

This is my dog.

He likes to give kisses.

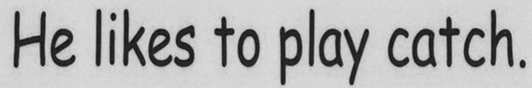

He likes to play catch.

# He never misses.

This
is
my
dog.

Now it's time for bed.

"Good-night", I say

Printed in Great Britain
by Amazon

14029189R10016